# Myths and legends

**Roderick Hunt**

Illustrated by
Victor Ambrus   Howard Bevan
Norma Burgin   Oliver Frey
Valerie Littlewood
Brian Melling   Lyn Mitchell
Christine Molan
Sandy Nightingale
Roger Payne   Joanna Troughton
Michael Whittlesea
Joe Wright

**Oxford University Press**

# Contents

| | |
|---|---|
| The princess and the pedlar | 3 |
| Horatius | 20 |
| But Liza . . . | 28 |
| The death of Balder | 34 |
| A moan too many | 48 |
| Cap o'Rushes | 50 |
| Count Horror | 68 |
| King Great Virtue | 72 |
| Canonbie Dick | 82 |
| The Mystery of Atlantis | 90 |
| How Banjuwangi got its name | 100 |
| How the lord chose a wife | 112 |
| Eros the secret husband | 116 |
| The legend of fair Rosamund | 124 |
| The emergency | 128 |

Oxford University Press, Walton Street, Oxford OX2 6DP   © Roderick Hunt 1981
Filmset by Tradespools Ltd, Frome, Somerset   Printed in Hong Kong
First published 1981   Reprinted 1983, 1985, 1987, 1988, 1990, 1993

# The princess and the pedlar

There was once a poor pedlar who travelled from place to place selling his wares.

He carried all his goods in a large sack and everything he owned in the whole world he took with him wherever he went.

Often the pedlar would sell nothing and would have no money. When this happened he would sleep in a barn, or lie among the leafy ferns in the woods with only the owls for company.

'What do I care,' he told himself, 'whether I have money or not? It seems to me that people who have money have far too much to worry about. I have none at all, yet I don't have a care in the world.'

Now you may think that because the pedlar had no home of his own and had very few possessions he was a useless, lazy, good-for-nothing sort of fellow.

Well, you would be wrong. Poor and carefree as he was, the pedlar had two wonderful gifts. The first was the gift of making people happy. The second was the gift of understanding animals.

Perhaps the two gifts were one and the same.

Whenever the pedlar went to a town or village people would make him welcome. It would not be long before children were laughing and dancing round him. Women would be smiling and giving him cakes, and the men would be chuckling and asking him to have a drink.

Whenever he was in the country the animals would welcome him too.

If he sat down in the woods or fields for a rest beneath a tree, a rabbit might hop up to him or a bird might fly down and perch on his shoulder.

He soon came to understand the animals and their language. He could chatter like a squirrel, whistle like a songbird, and grunt like a badger.

When he called them, the animals would come to him, and the pedlar was never happier than when this happened.

Now the king of this land had a daughter who was very, very beautiful. She was so lovely that princes and noblemen came from many lands hoping to win favour with the king and marry the beautiful princess.

Unfortunately, the princess was very selfish and spoilt, which is hardly surprising since she had so much attention.

None of the suitors who came to the palace hoping to win the princess, however, could please her for long.

After a while she grew bored and then she grew sulky and bad-tempered. 'I'm bored! Bored! Bored!' she would shout.

The king would pace up and down in a state of agitation. 'Find something to amuse the princess,' he ordered. 'There's no pleasing her. In this mood her face will turn all the milk sour.'

At once rich noblemen hurried to the palace with wonderful gifts made of gold or silver or precious jewels.

Princes came with all manner of exotic presents such as silks and perfumes from the East, proud horses from Arabia or tigers from India.

Wise men came bringing books and papers, hoping to interest the princess with new things to learn.

Clever men tried to amuse her with all kinds of tricks and puzzles and diversions.

The princess would be interested for a little. Then she would stamp her feet and shout that she was bored, bored, bored.

In desparation, the king sent out a proclamation to be read throughout the land. It said this:

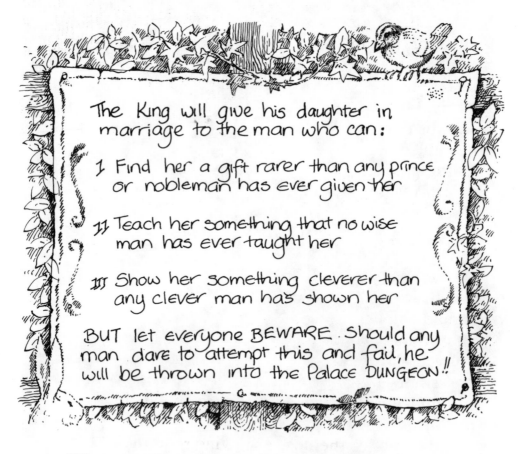

The King will give his daughter in marriage to the man who can:

I Find her a gift rarer than any prince or nobleman has ever given her

II Teach her something that no wise man has ever taught her

III Show her something cleverer than any clever man has shown her

BUT let everyone BEWARE. Should any man dare to attempt this and fail, he will be thrown into the Palace DUNGEON!!

When people heard the proclamation they said, 'That's a tall order. The princess is so difficult to please. It will take a very special kind of man to carry all that out.'

It so happened that the pedlar had not heard the king's proclamation, but one day was passing the palace carrying his sack over his shoulder.

8

As he walked by the palace garden wall, he heard the sound of someone crying.

Being a carefree sort of fellow the pedlar couldn't bear to hear anyone unhappy so, without a thought, he climbed on to the wall and jumped down into the garden.

There he saw the beautiful princess crying bitterly. Of course her eyes were swollen and her nose was red with crying so she didn't look quite so beautiful.

'Jumping over the wall does not amuse me,' said the princess huffily. 'Nothing in your sack will interest me and I shouldn't imagine a rough fellow like you can teach me anything. I'll have you thrown in the dungeon.'

'Wait a minute,' exclaimed the pedlar. 'I only came to see why you were crying. I don't see why I should end up having bed and breakfast in the dungeon for that.'

'Haven't you heard the proclamation?' said the princess crossly. She took out a piece of paper and handed it to the pedlar. 'Well, you'd better be thrown in the dungeon in any case.'

'Hold on,' cried the pedlar, having read the piece of paper. 'If you intend to throw me into the dungeon anyway, I might as well do what it says on the proclamation.'

Before the princess had time to cry out, the pedlar picked her up and threw her over his shoulder. Then he scaled the wall like a cat and carried her off before she could say '. . . !'

She was no heavier than his sack so he ran with
her across the fields and meadows and came at last
to the wood.

'Put me down! Put me down!' screamed the princess
drumming her fists on the pedlar's back.

'First I'll find you a gift rarer than any prince
or nobleman has ever given you,' he said and he
searched among the leaves and at last found
growing there, a tiny snowdrop with a bead of dew
sparkling on its petals.

'This is the first snowdrop of the year,' he said.

'Pooh!' scoffed the princess. 'That doesn't
seem like much.'

'Then let me teach you something that no wise
man has ever taught you,' said the pedlar.

He put the princess over his knee and spanked
her as hard as he could.

The princess cried at the top of her lungs
so the pedlar spanked her again.

And would you believe it? The princess stopped
crying and looked again at the snowdrop, growing
out of the earth.

'Why, it is very beautiful,' she said.

The pedlar took her hand and led her to
a bush. 'Be very quiet,' he told her.

As they watched, they saw two birds building a
nest with tiny twigs and pieces of dry grass.

'Is that something cleverer than any clever
man can show you?'

The princess gave a tiny smile. 'It is very
clever,' she said.

The pedlar told the princess not to move or make a sound. Then he called two squirrels that lived in a tree close by. The squirrels ran down the tree and on to his outstretched arm.

They sat, one on each of his shoulders, and nibbled at some crusts of bread he found for them in his pocket.

Then he whistled and a bird flew down and landed on his head. He looked so comic with a bird perched on his head and two squirrels munching on his shoulders that the princess could not help laughing out loud.

At once the bird flew off and the squirrels chased back up into the trees.

The princess's eyes began to shine. 'I think that is the most wonderful thing I have ever seen in my life,' she said. 'What else can you show me?'

The pedlar took the princess and showed her the green buds swelling on the trees. He showed her catkins and tiny shoots beginning to push their way up through the ground.

They went to a barn where the first spring lambs were being born and they found a nest with three warm, green, speckled eggs.

Not once did the princess feel unhappy and not once was she bored.

'I have spent the best afternoon of my life,' she said as they arrived back at the palace gates. 'My father can send out a proclamation saying that we are to be married next month. What do you say to that?'

But when the princess looked round, the pedlar had gone.

'Surely he wanted to marry me!' she cried. But she was wrong. The pedlar led far too carefree a life to want to settle down in a rich palace married to a princess.

Now the princess was unhappy for a different reason. She had fallen in love with the pedlar and dearly longed to marry him.

She made the king send out proclamation after proclamation seeking information about the pedlar. A large sum of money was offered as a reward for anyone who could find him.

It was no use. Nowhere was he to be found.

'He was the only man ever to make me happy,'
sighed the princess. 'I would give my soul to
the Devil if only I could have him.'

Later that day, a man appeared suddenly in the
palace garden.

'Who are you?' asked the princess, startled by
the figure who stood beside her.

'Let us say I am someone who could find the
pedlar for you,' smiled the man.

'Really!' exclaimed the princess. 'I said I
would sell my soul to the Devil if only I could
have him.'

'And do you mean it?'

'I do,' replied the princess.

'Well, as it happens, I am the Devil himself.
Sign in blood on this piece of paper and I will
bring the pedlar to you.'

'But will he love me?' asked the princess.

'I think that can be arranged,' replied the Devil. 'How long do you want me to give you before I come and fetch you? Shall we say twenty years?'

'Oh yes,' cried the princess and without thinking she signed the paper with blood pricked from her own finger.

Almost at once the Devil whisked the pedlar into the garden and made him fall in love with the princess.

Then the princess and the pedlar went to see the king and received his blessing.

Before long the wedding bells were ringing.

The years rolled by and, just as the Devil had
promised, the pedlar loved his wife. Soon they
had children, and they were very happy.

Sometimes the princess remembered her pact with
the Devil, but she kept putting the thought out
of her mind.

'Twenty years is a long time,' she told herself.

At last the old king died and the pedlar became
ruler in his place. Of course he was a good king
because he was such a happy sort of person.

Everyone around him was happy too, and so all
the kingdom was happy.

But time passed quickly. Soon nineteen years
had sped by and only one was left.

The princess, who was now queen of course,
became very afraid. She could not sleep at
night and she grew pale and ill.

Often the king asked his wife what it was that
worried her but she did not dare not tell him.

At last the twenty years were up, all except
one day. The queen locked herself in her room
so that her husband and the children would not
see her weeping.

In the morning the Devil appeared, just as
he had said he would, to claim her for his own.

'Please give me one more day,' begged the
queen. 'I have many matters to see to and I have
not yet said goodbye to my husband and children.'

At that moment there was a rattling on the
chamber door. It was the queen's husband.

The Devil did not want to be seen by the pedlar
for he did not care for good, kind, happy people,
so he quickly agreed to let the wife have
one more day. Then he disappeared.

Being the kind of man he was, the pedlar
noticed a strange, sulphery kind of smell in
the room and he guessed correctly that his wife
must have a pact with the Devil.

Over the years the pedlar had really grown to
love his wife and he had enjoyed being the king,
so he said to his wife, 'Let me meet the Devil
when he comes for you. I will try to think of
a way to trick him.'

The Devil came again the next night but
instead of finding the queen in her room he found
the pedlar.

'Good evening,' said the pedlar politely.
'You may take my wife if you must, but I'll make
a deal with you. If I can find a task which you
find impossible to accomplish, will you cancel
the pact with her?'

'Since there is nothing I cannot accomplish,'
replied the Devil, 'I agree. Find me something
I cannot do and I will set your wife free of
her pact with me.'

'Very well,' said the pedlar. 'Here are three
golden hairs from the head of my wife. 'Take them
and make them ten times as long. You must not
tie them. You must stretch them until they are
long enough.'

At this the Devil flew into a furious rage.
For all his powers, the one thing he could not
do was to make the hairs longer. They were already
so fine that if he stretched them they would break
and if he hammered them he would crush them.

The pedlar had outwitted him, and there was
nothing for the Devil to do but give back the
piece of paper which the queen had signed.

I'll bet you know how this story ends. The pedlar
and his wife went on living as king and queen
and, with their fine children, they lived happily
ever after.

# Horatius

The great wooden bridge across the river Tiber
shook and vibrated. The air rang with the steady
pounding of axes as men and soldiers frantically
chopped through the heavy supports.

The bridge was the only means of entry into
Rome. But it must be cut down if the city was to
be saved from destruction and the people from
being slaughtered.

From the city walls the two Consuls who ruled
Rome stared anxiously into the distance. They had
been watching for some time a cloud of dust made
by the feet of the advancing Tuscan army.

The cloud of dust drew nearer and nearer. Still
the bridge was standing. Already the Consuls
could see the glint of the sun on shield and spear as
the Tuscan soldiers approached.

A messenger arrived. His chest was heaving and his clothes were covered with dust and blood. He scrambled up to the Consuls.

'King Tarquin rides with Lars Porsena. They have an army of eighty thousand foot soldiers and ten thousand horsemen. Nothing now stands between them and the city.'

The Consuls already knew that they could not stop the enemy. They had seen their army beaten back. But they were staggered at the strength of Lars Porsena's forces.

'So proud Tarquin, once king of this city, hopes to enter it again,' they said. 'It will be a sad moment for those still alive to see it.'

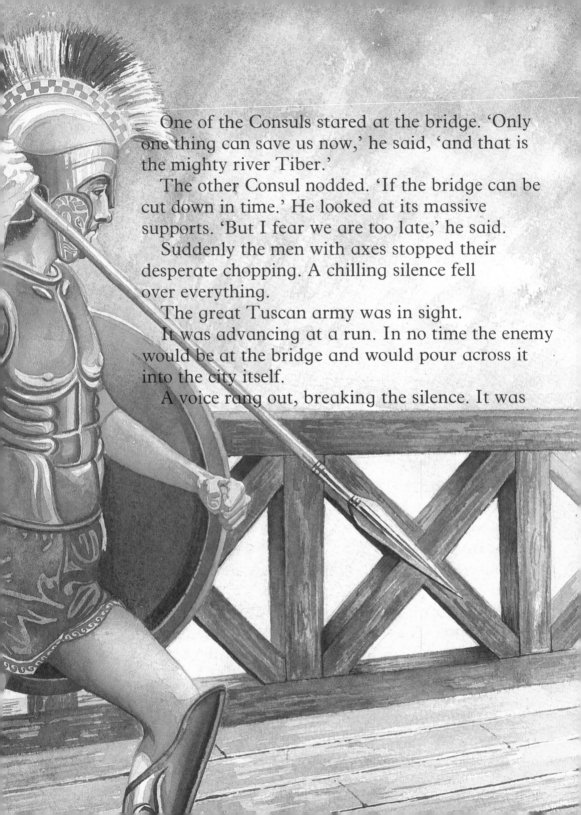

One of the Consuls stared at the bridge. 'Only one thing can save us now,' he said, 'and that is the mighty river Tiber.'

The other Consul nodded. 'If the bridge can be cut down in time.' He looked at its massive supports. 'But I fear we are too late,' he said.

Suddenly the men with axes stopped their desperate chopping. A chilling silence fell over everything.

The great Tuscan army was in sight.

It was advancing at a run. In no time the enemy would be at the bridge and would pour across it into the city itself.

A voice rang out, breaking the silence. It was

a famous soldier called Horatius Cocles. 'A man can only die once,' he shouted. 'What better way than in defending his beloved city?'

'The bridge is narrow. Three men will be able to hold back the attackers for a short time. I will stand in the middle. Who will take a place on either side of me?'

At once two other soldiers, Herminius and Spurius Lartius stepped forward. Together the three men drew their swords and walked to the end of the bridge.

'Continue to cut down the bridge,' called Horatius. 'We will hold them off for as long as we can stand.'

Soon the vanguard of the invading army swept up and halted only a short distance away. Lars Porsena was seated in an ivory chariot.

By his side rode Tarquin on a mighty war horse and next to him was his son, Sextus.

When the Tuscans saw that they only had three men to face, a great shout of scornful laughter went up.

Three Tuscan soldiers, keen to win themselves glory, drew their swords and rushed at the Romans.

Lartius neatly shouldered one into the river. Herminius finished the other with his sword while Horatius side-stepped and thrust his dagger into the third.

Three more Tuscans came forward. The brave Romans put paid to them as easily as they had the first three.

Then a huge Tuscan soldier stepped up. Angrily he shouted, 'Let me clear a path through these children of the she-wolf.'

With that he ran at Horatius, flailing his sword like a madman. Horatius parried with his shield but the sword caught him savagely in the thigh.

Crippled by pain, Horatius thrust his sword at the Tuscan's throat and pierced him through.

Then from behind came a great creaking sound. 'The bridge is falling,' Horatius shouted. 'Run Lartius! Run Herminius! Run for your lives!'

Lartius and Herminius reached safety but Horatius waited to hold back any further attack.

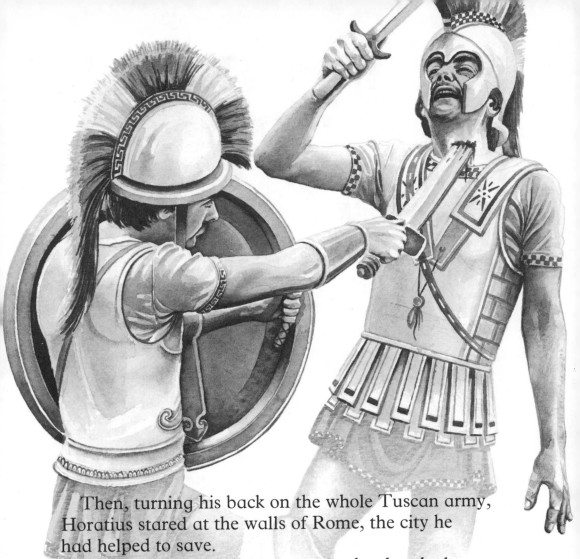

Then, turning his back on the whole Tuscan army,
Horatius stared at the walls of Rome, the city he
had helped to save.

His lips moved in silent prayer as he sheathed
his sword. Then he plunged into the raging waters
of the river.

'Oh Tiber! Father Tiber!' he called. 'A Roman's
life is in your hands today.'

The river, swollen high by months of rain, swept
Horatius under. Kicking desperately, he
struggled to the surface and tried to swim
for his life.

Horatius was weakened by the wound in his thigh and weighed down by his heavy armour. He felt himself being pulled under.

Somehow he found the strength to fight the raging current and, almost miraculously, managed to keep afloat.

'Drown, curse you, drown,' snarled Sextus from the bank.

'Where is your soldier's honour?' rebuked Lars Porsena. 'May he reach the shore safely. A man as brave as that deserves to live.'

At long last Horatius struggled to the far bank where many willing hands pulled him to safety.

Lars Porsena saw now that he would never take Rome. To cross the river he would have to march his army for many days before they came to a ford.

By that time Rome would be put in a proper state of defence.

Lars Porsena gave up the attempt and returned to his own land.

As for Horatius, he was carried in triumph through the city. The Consuls told him that he was to have some of the land that he had rescued from their enemies.

They awarded him as much land as he could plough with oxen in one day.

And, in the centre of Rome, a statue was set up in honour of Horatius who defied a mighty army and saved a city.

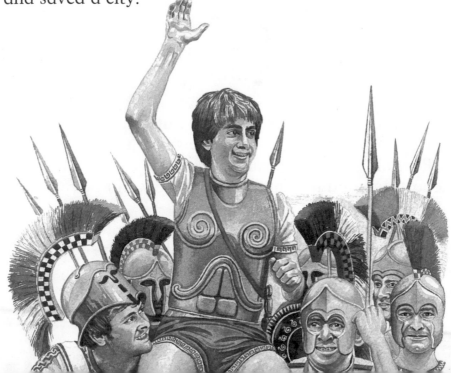

# But Liza . . .

Jake was a quiet sort of fellow, but when he married Liza everyone shook their heads.

'Poor old Jake,' they said. 'Liza is so headstrong and argumentative, Jake won't have a life of his own.'

It was true. Liza had been nice enough to Jake when they were courting, but once they were married, she soon showed Jake just how contrary she was.

Jake quickly saw that he was never going to get his own way. Whatever he told her to do she would do the opposite. Whenever he wanted to do something she would put a stop to it.

'If there's any bossing around to be done,' Liza snapped, 'I'll do the bossing!'

For a while Jake stood his wife's stubborn and domineering ways as meekly as he could.

At last he thought to himself, 'I was better off before I was married. At least I could enjoy myself once in a while and have a few friends round now and again for a bite to eat and a drop to drink.

'I don't suppose my Liza would ever agree to anything like that. If I asked her she'd just snap my head off.'

As he thought this, Jake had a very clever idea.

That same evening, Jake spoke to Liza as they sat by the fire.

'I can't think why folk should ever want to have people round to their houses. All they do is drink up all the drink and eat up all the food. Think what it must cost.'

'Are you saying we can't afford to ask people round to our house?' snapped Liza. 'We'll have some round on Saturday.'

Jake wanted to smile but he pulled a long face. 'But Liza, what will we give them to drink? We don't want them to start on our best cider, now do we?'

Liza sniffed, 'And why not may I ask? You can go down to the cellar tomorrow and tap our best barrel.'

Jake said, 'But Liza, if we drink the best cider I don't think we should give folk anything to eat.'

'We'll do things properly,' cried Liza firmly. 'I'll start baking tomorrow.'

'But Liza,' said Jake, gloomily. 'We'd better not ask too many people. Just one or two.'

'Do you want folk to think we're mean?' asked Liza. 'I say we'll have a party and it will be a really good party too.'

'But Liza-' said Jake.

'No more "buts",' said Liza finally. 'We're having a party.'

'If you say so,' said Jake, pretending to look thoroughly depressed about the whole idea but laughing up his sleeve all the time.

That Saturday, Jake enjoyed himself at the party more than anyone else. In fact he had such a good time that Liza secretly wondered if he hadn't played some kind of trick on her.

After this Liza became even more bossy and even more awkward than ever. She would argue with Jake about almost everything.

That spring it rained a good deal and the river became so swollen it was almost up to the top of the bank.

One day Jake and Liza walked in to the village. They took a short cut and came to a narrow bridge over the gushing river.

'That bridge doesn't look too safe,' said Jake. 'Perhaps we'd better go back the long way and cross the stone bridge.'

'Nonsense!' snapped Liza. 'We'll not waste our time. This bridge is quite safe.'

And she began to walk across it.

Suddenly Jake noticed that one or two of the planks were loose. 'Mind your step, Liza,' he called out.

'I'll mind my step and you can mind your business, Jake,' called Liza. 'This bridge is perfectly sa—'

But as she spoke the planks gave way and she fell through into the racing water and disappeared.

Jake blinked once or twice then rushed upstream as fast as he could shouting, 'Liza! Liza!'

Two men along the bank saw him and called, 'What are you shouting like that for?'

'My wife has fallen into the river,' panted Jake.

'Why you cloth-head,' shouted the men. 'She will have been swept downstream, not up.'

'Ah!' called Jake. 'You don't know my Liza. She is so obstinate and contrary that she is bound to be going against the current!'

# The death of Balder

Of all the gods of the Norsemen, the best loved was Balder.

His face was dazzling to look at. His smile was radiant and his eyes shone with warmth and kindness.

One night, Balder had a dream which filled him with terror and dread. When he awoke, the dream would not leave him, and his heart was heavy.

'What troubles you?' asked his wife, Nanna. 'A cloud seems to hang over you. It dims your brightness and chills your warmth.'

'Alas,' said Balder. 'There is a shadow in my heart which will not go away.'

Nanna was frightened when she heard Balder speak like this.

'Go to Odin, your father,' she begged. 'He is king of the gods. Together you must talk to Frigga your mother. Tell them of this dread which has come upon you.'

Balder went to Valhalla, the hall where Odin and Frigga lived. When Odin and Frigga saw how downcast Balder was, they were shocked.

Frigga turned pale and turned to Odin in fear. 'I feel a shadow on Balder's heart,' she gasped. 'It is the shadow of death. Oh my son! I fear for you.'

'If I am to meet death. I will do so bravely,' said Balder. But his bright face shone no more.

'Wait!' cried Odin. 'This dreadful thing *must* not happen. Let us call a meeting of all the gods and seek their counsel.'

Odin summoned the gods and when they heard of Balder's dream and the dark shadow he felt inside him, a chill passed over them as if an icy wind had blown.

'Can we not find out for certain if Balder's dreams are not just a passing thing?' asked the gods.

Odin's face grew sad and a furrow appeared on his brow.

'Before this meeting,' he said gravely, 'I went myself, in secret, to the Land of the Dead. There I saw a hall set out in readiness for a great feast as if to await the coming of an honoured guest.

'I spoke to the prophetess Volva. She told me that the feast was to await the coming of Balder. How or when he is to die, she would not tell me.'

The gods sighed. Odin's words were almost more than they could bear.

'Balder shall not die,' said Frigga. 'Am I not the queen? Everything must obey me. I will send word for everything on the earth to come to me and promise not to harm my son. If Balder cannot be hurt, he cannot be killed.'

At once Frigga sent out her command. 'Tell everything in the earth to come before me now,' she said. 'They must swear never to hurt Balder the bright and beautiful.'

And so all things on the earth came to her as she had ordered. Every one of them swore an oath never to harm Balder.

Fire, water, iron and all metals, stones and
earth, trees, plants, sicknesses, poisons, beasts,
birds and all living things bowed down and
promised her what she commanded.

When this was done, the Queen of Asgard smiled.
'Balder is safe,' she declared. 'Now nothing can
harm him.'

When Balder told Frigga that he still felt the heavy shadow in his heart, Frigga reassured him. 'The feeling will pass,' she said. 'There is now nothing that can bring you death.'

Odin still feared for Balder but he did not speak of this.

The gods made much of the fact that everything on earth had sworn not to hurt Balder. 'No spear will pierce him, no sword will cut him, no stone will bruise him,' they said. 'Let us make sport of this.'

They took Balder to the green outside the city of Asgard and stood him in the middle of it.

They they took out their weapons and hurled them at Balder. Every spear they threw glanced away and clanged to the ground. Every stone they hurled bounced off doing Balder no harm.

Balder stood laughing at the sport. His face was bright once more. The terrible dread that had been in his heart was forgotten in the enjoyment of the game.

Now the gods took out their swords and they hacked at Balder. But not one sword would touch him for the metal had sworn never to harm him.

Then they fetched heavy wood sticks and clubs to beat him with. They beat him so hard that the sticks and clubs broke in half but the wood refused to injure him.

'You cannot hurt me,' laughed Balder. 'You will only tire yourself.'

But the gods were enjoying the game. They went on with it, cheering and shouting.

The wicked god Loki was out of favour with Odin and Frigga. He knew nothing of all this.

When he heard the shouts and laughter he went to see what the other gods were doing.

'How can this be?' cried Loki. 'Do you mean to kill Balder? Do you love him no more?'

'This is only a game,' panted Tyr. 'Everything has promised Frigga that it will not hurt Balder. However hard we throw things at him or hack at him with sticks or swords, it has no effect. There is nothing that will break its promise to Frigga. Balder is quite safe from all harm.'

Loki hated the beautiful god Balder. He was jealous of his beauty, and jealous of the love and warmth everyone gave him.

'Can it really be true that everything has promised not to hurt Balder?' he wondered.

In his scheming mind he thought of a way to find out from Frigga if this was true.

He knew the queen would never receive him. He was out of favour because of his misdeeds. So he changed himself into an old woman and went to the palace.

Frigga was seated on her throne when Loki came before her. She looked down kindly on the poor old woman and invited her to sit down.

'Have you come from far?' she asked.

'Yes,' replied Loki, 'and I saw something I could not understand as I entered the gates of Asgard.'

'Tell me what you saw,' said Frigga.

Loki's eyes gleamed mischievously.

'I saw Balder the bright and
beautiful on the green outside the city,' said Loki.
'The gods were throwing spears at him
but Balder stood there unharmed.'

'The gods are playing a new game,' said Frigga,
smiling. 'You see everything has promised never to
hurt Balder, so whatever is thrown at him will not
hurt him and he cannot be killed.'

'Did you say that everything promised you this?'
asked Loki, craftily. 'Every single thing?'

'Well, one thing did not promise,' said Frigga.
'It is something so small and weak that I did not
bother to ask it. It cannot harm Balder.'

'What is that one thing?' asked Loki innocently.

Frigga did not realise that the old woman was
the wicked god. Without a second thought,
she answered, 'That one thing is the mistletoe
plant. I cannot see how that can hurt my son.'

Loki knew that mistletoe grew near the palace. With shining eyes he begged leave of Frigga and went at once to the tree where the mistletoe grew.

Here he changed himself back into his own shape and cut the thickest sprig of mistletoe he could find.

Then he took the stem and fashioned it into a deadly throwing dart. Having done this he went to join the gods who were still playing on the green.

For a while Loki watched them secretly. He did not want the gods to see him throw the mistletoe dart at the bright god. If he hurt their beloved Balder they would be bound to fall on him in anger and fury.

If only he could get someone else to throw
the dart.

Looking round the group of gods he saw Hodur
the twin brother of Balder. Hodur was blind and
could not see to join in the new game.

Loki quietly went up to the blind god. 'Would
you like to join in?' he asked. 'Feel how sturdy
and sharp this dart is. Why not throw that at
Balder?'

'You know that I am blind,' said Hodur. 'Then
how can I throw?'

'I will guide your arm. Just throw the dart as
hard as you can,' said Loki.

Hodur did as Loki said. He drew back his arm
and threw the dart with all his might. The
deadly weapon struck Balder and pierced him
through the heart.

Balder let out a gasp and slumped lifeless to the ground.

The gods cried out in amazement and confusion while evil Loki slipped away leaving Hodur to cry, 'What has happened? Has Balder been hurt? Tell me what has happened someone.'

The gods returned to the city of Asgard. Silently they approached Valhalla and there saw Frigga seated on her throne.

How were they to tell her?

Frigga, however, saw their tearful eyes and knew that something terrible had happened.

'Balder is dead,' wept Hodur bitterly. 'He died by my hand, but it was Loki who killed him. Why did I not guess that Loki meant him harm?'

Some of the gods searched in anger for Loki but he was nowhere to be found.

Balder's body was taken to the shore. Here it was placed on his huge ship, Ringhorn. Then all was made ready for Balder's last journey.

It was the Norse custom to place a dead man on his own ship then set fire to it and let the burning ship sail out to sea.

The gods placed Balder's body on Ringhorn and gave it due honours. But the ship proved too heavy for them to move. Not even Thor was able to slide it forward a single fraction.

'Send for the giantess Hyrrockin,' commanded Odin. 'She must push the great ship out to sea.'

Hyrrockin arrived riding a savage wolf. At Odin's request she placed her great hands on

the stern of the longship. Then she pushed it
with such force that sparks flashed from the
keel as it sped down the beach to the sea.

Sadly the gods watched the blazing ship floating
away on the waves to disappear as a faint glow
in the approaching darkness.

Meanwhile, Odin had sent Hermod, the messenger of the gods to visit Hel in her underground kingdom.

Hel was the queen of the Land of the Dead and she had the power to release Balder from the dead.

Hermod begged Hel to restore Balder to them. He told her what grief and sorrow there was both on earth and in Asgard because of Balder's death.

Hel agreed to do this providing everything there was would weep for Balder, just as everything had promised not to harm him.

Should one single thing not weep for the bright god, Hel would never return Balder to life.

When Hermod returned to Asgard with this news, Odin sent out at once that everything should weep for Balder. And all things wept. Every living creature, every rock, plant and tree wept, and there was sorrow everywhere.

Odin sent out again to see if everything that was had shed tears for Balder.

But as the messengers hurried back to tell him this was so, they passed a cave in which they saw an old hag crouching on the floor.

'Have you no tears to shed for Balder?' they asked the witch.

'There will be no tears from me,' she cried. 'I had no love for him. Let Hel keep him.' And with an evil laugh she was gone.

Sadly the messengers bore the news that all things had wept for Balder. All, that is, except for one horrible old witch whose laugh, they told Odin, was just like that of the wicked god Loki.

# A moan too many

A king once had a fine ship built. The ship was
to be the pride of his fleet. When it was finished
the king was so delighted with it that he invited
his ministers and a number of important guests
to take a short voyage with him to try it out.

During the voyage a slight wind sprang up and
the ship started to roll a little.

Suddenly one of the guests, who was nervous of
the sea, began to moan and cry out, 'There's going
to be a storm. The ship will capsize.'

The wind grew just a little bit stronger and the
ship rose and fell. 'Oh . . . ooooh,' cried the man.
'We're all going to drown.'

The king frowned in annoyance. The man's moans
and groans were spoiling his enjoyment.

The man began to cry out even more. 'Oooh . . .'
he moaned, 'I know we're going to sink!'

To everyone's amazement, the king ordered the
man to be thrown overboard into the sea.

The man went under and came up giving a tremendous yell. 'HELP! I CAN'T SWIM!'

The king commanded the man be rescued at once and given dry clothes to wear.

From that moment on the man didn't groan or moan once. He was quiet for the rest of the voyage.

'You see,' said the king, 'when the man was in the sea he really did have reason to moan. As soon as he was back on board he realised how safe and secure he was after all.'

It's often easy to moan but, when you think about it, you could be in a much worse situation.

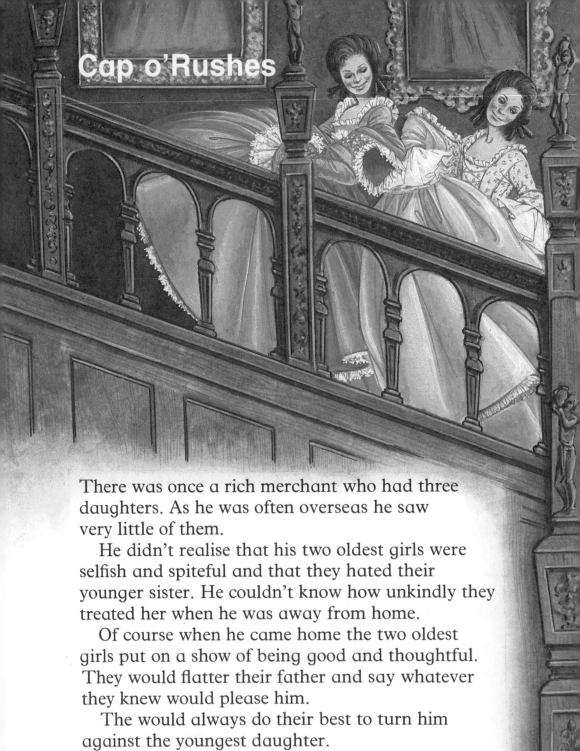

# Cap o'Rushes

There was once a rich merchant who had three
daughters. As he was often overseas he saw
very little of them.

He didn't realise that his two oldest girls were
selfish and spiteful and that they hated their
younger sister. He couldn't know how unkindly they
treated her when he was away from home.

Of course when he came home the two oldest
girls put on a show of being good and thoughtful.
They would flatter their father and say whatever
they knew would please him.

The would always do their best to turn him
against the youngest daughter.

The merchant always liked to bring presents home for his three girls and this time he brought each one a beautiful dress.

'Why these dresses are simply too wonderful for words!' cooed the oldest daughters. 'We shall put them on at once and wear them all day.'

And they ran upstairs to change into them.

The youngest daughter folded her dress and put it back into its box.

'Are you not going to put your dress on too?' demanded the merchant.

'Oh Father,' the youngest girl said. 'I should spoil such a beautiful dress if I wore it now. I'll save it and wear it to a ball.'

The merchant's face clouded with anger. 'You ungrateful girl!' he exclaimed. 'Your sisters are pleased with their dresses. I see you don't care for yours. Perhaps your sisters are right to call you a trouble maker. Now go to your room and put on your dress at once.'

51

When the daughters came back in their fine dresses the youngest one's eyes were red from crying.

'Look at Miss Misery-face,' scoffed the two other daughters. 'You would think she'd be as happy as we are to have a new dress.'

The merchant beamed with pleasure. 'Well, I'm sure you all love your old father,' he said, as the oldest daughter stroked his hair.

Suddenly he had an idea. 'Tell me,' he said, 'how much do you all love me?'

The oldest daughter was quick to reply. 'Why, I love you more than all the gold in the world.'

The second-oldest daughter put on her sweetest smile. 'And I love you more than all the silver in the world,' she said.

Tears welled up in the merchant's eyes. He turned to his youngest daughter. 'And how about you, my dear? How much do you love me?'

The youngest daughter thought carefully. At last she said, 'I love you as much as fresh meat loves salt.'

'What!' cried the merchant angrily. 'If that's all you can say then you don't love me at all.'

He smashed his fist on a small table beside his chair.

'My other daughters make me feel proud of their love, but you break my heart. You are thoughtless and ungrateful. Leave my house at once. I never want to see you again.'

The poor girl rushed from the house in tears.

She did not stop running until she was many miles from her home. Then she collapsed sobbing beside a tiny stream.

It was a long time before she was able to go on. At last she came to a small cottage. There an old woman let her have a cloak and hood woven from rushes. In exchange the girl gave her the ring she wore on her finger.

Then she tied up her long golden hair in a kerchief. She put the rush cloak on over her dress and pulled the hood up over her face.

On the other side of the hill stood a big mansion. She went to the back door and spoke to the cook. 'Do you need a maid?' she asked.

'No,' said the cook. 'We don't need any more servants.'

'Please,' begged the girl. 'I don't want any wages and I'll do any kind of work. I've just got nowhere to go.'

The cook felt sorry for the girl and allowed
her to stay as a slavey.

'It will mean dirty work,' she said. 'You'll
have to scrub the floors, black the cooking range,
polish the brass and wash greasy pans. Can you do
all those things?'

'I'll do them gladly,' said the girl, 'as long
as I have somewhere to live.'

She was given a tiny back room to sleep in.
Carefully she hid her beautiful dress. The next
day she was up early, dressed in her rush cape and
hood. She had never done dirty work before, but
she did not mind.

At first the other servants laughed at the
strange girl in her cape of rushes. But she was
cheerful and hardworking and they quite liked
her. They called her Cap o' Rushes.

55

The weeks went by and Cap o' Rushes worked as hard as ever. She cleaned and scrubbed, she swept and polished.

The pots and pans, the floor and windows, even the big black cooking-range gleamed as they had never done before.

But often at night, Cap o' Rushes would lie in her narrow bed in her small bare room and cry bitter tears. Sometimes she would take out her beautiful dress and gaze at it with a sad longing.

'What a strange girl you are,' the cook once said to her. 'All you ever wear is your rush cape and hood. You hardly every show your face.

'Your hair is always tied back. I don't even know what colour it is. But still, you work hard, so I won't pry into your affairs.'

One day there was great excitement among all the
servants. The lord had told them that he was to
hold a ball for his son.

The cook began to busy herself in the kitchen.
'There will be a lot to do,' she said, 'with all
the food to prepare.'

Cap o' Rushes was told to polish all the silver
and shine the glasses.

'Won't it be wonderful,' cried the cook. 'All
the servants are allowed to watch the ball from the
gallery. Then you'll see how young and handsome
the lord's son is, Cap o' Rushes.'

On the day of the ball the cook said, 'I am sorry, Cap o' Rushes, but we all have to dress in our best clothes to watch the ball. All you have to wear is your rush cape. I'm afraid you'll have to stay behind in the kitchen.'

Sadly Cap o' Rushes watched the servants go. Then she sat by the cooking range and a great big tear ran down her face.

Suddenly an idea came to her. If she couldn't go to the ball as a servant in her cape of rushes then she would go as a lady in her beautiful dress.

Quickly she ran to the tap and washed her long golden hair. When it was dry, she went to her room and put on the dress.

With a beating heart she made her way up to the ballroom and pushed open the doors.

As she appeared in the ballroom, people stopped dancing to look at her. 'What a beautiful girl,' they exclaimed to each other. 'She must be a princess.'

The lord's son was astonished by her beauty. He hurried across the ballroom and took her hand. 'I don't know who you are or where you are from, but will you be my partner in the next dance?'

Even before the dance had finished he had quite fallen in love with her. And he danced with her for the rest of the evening.

Just before the ball ended, Cap o' Rushes slipped away. She ran back to her room and changed into her rush cape just as she was before the ball.

The servants found her pretending to be asleep in front of the embers of the cooking-range.

They could talk of nothing else but the beautiful and mysterious girl who had danced all evening with the lord's son.

'You should have seen her, Cap o' Rushes,' they said. 'No one knew who she was. Some say she was a fairy princess. Anyway, the lord's son wants to hold another ball next week. He hopes his fairy princess will appear again.'

A week later the second ball was held. Again the servants hurried off to watch it. Cap o' Rushes waited to put on her beautiful dress. Then she appeared when the ball was half-way through.

'You are the most beautiful girl in the world,' said the lord's son as he danced with her. 'Please marry me. If you don't I shall die.'

He slipped a ring on her finger.

'But you know nothing of me,' said Cap o' Rushes.

'I know I love you, and that is all that matters,' said the lord's son.

When no one was looking, Cap o' Rushes slipped away from the ballroom and was back in her old rush cape before the cook and the servants were back from the ball.

'I think the lord's son has found a fairy princess,' said one of the servants. 'She vanished again tonight before the ball had ended.'

The next day, the kitchen was full of the news.
The young lord was out searching for the beautiful
girl who had been at the ball.

Day after day he searched but she was nowhere to
be found. At last he took to his bed and refused
to eat anything.

One morning the lord himself came into the kitchen. 'My son will become really ill unless someone can get him to eat something,' he said.

'I'll make him a dish of gruel,' said the cook. 'That's just the thing for someone dying of love.'

Cap o' Rushes pricked up her ears. The young lord had really meant it when he told her he would die if she didn't marry him. Now she knew his love was true.

When the cook wasn't looking, she dropped the ring the lord's son had given her into the gruel.

The young lord ate the gruel and found, to his surprise, the ring at the bottom of the dish.

At once he sprang out of bed and dressed himself as quickly as he could.

'Send for the cook,' he ordered, 'for she will tell me who my loved one is.'

The cook's face went bright red as she was called into the young lord's room. 'I've been cook here for forty years,' she said, 'and no one's ever complained about my cooking before.'

The young lord held up the ring. 'It was the best gruel I ever ate,' he said, 'for it contained this ring to cure my lovesickness.'

'Well I never did!' exclaimed the cook. 'I never saw that ring in all my life, and if you think I allow things like that in my cooking . . .'

'Don't you see?' cried the young man. 'I gave this ring to the girl who came to the ball. Now it appears in my gruel. Who else was in the kitchen when you made it?'

'Only Cap o' Rushes, sir,' replied the cook, 'a strange girl who came from nowhere and works as a slavey.'

'Call for her at once,' said the young lord. Cap o' Rushes was sent for and at last came in with her face still partly hidden by the rush hood of her cape.

The lord's son went up to her and slowly pulled back the hood. He untied her long golden hair and gently held her face in his hands.

'So, my fairy princess is the slavey in my father's kitchen. You are not a fairy after all and you shall not be a slavey any longer. I love you, Cap o' Rushes, and ask you to be my wife.'

And so their wedding day was planned, and Cap o' Rushes was the happiest of girls.

She found out that her father had returned from one of his long sea voyages and she invited him to the wedding.

Before the feast was prepared, Cap o' Rushes went to the cook and told her to make each dish containing meat, twice. One dish was to have no salt and the other was to be seasoned normally.

When the wedding guests were seated and the food was served the guests could scarcely contain their amazement. The food was completely tasteless.

When they looked on the table for salt, they found that none had been put out.

Some of them began to complain and grumble, for the food was not fit to eat.

Then Cap o' Rushes' father stood up. 'Listen to me,' he said. 'Hear how foolish a father can be. Once I brought home presents for my daughters. In my pride, I asked them how much they loved me.

'The eldest said she loved me as more than all the gold in the world. Yet when I was away she left home and took all my gold with her.

'The second said she loved me more than all the silver in the world, yet she took all my silver and left me too.

'When my youngest daughter said that she loved me as much as fresh meat loves salt, I did not realise that she loved me best of all.'

With tears in his eyes, the old man begged Cap o' Rushes to forgive him.

'Just as fresh meat loves salt,' said Cap o' Rushes, 'so our guests would love their dishes seasoned.' She signalled to the servants who brought in the second meal the cook had prepared.

Then she forgave her father, and because the two other sisters had stolen all their father's money she invited him to come and live with her at the big house.

'Now I indeed know you love me as much as meat loves salt,' her father said.

# Count Horror

Of all the characters in horror stories one of the best known is Count Dracula, the gruesome bloodsucking count, in his grim, forbidding castle in the mysterious country of Transylvania.

Count Dracula was invented by a writer named Bram Stoker.

Little did Stoker think when he wrote his book *Dracula*, in 1897, that almost a hundred years later the evil count would still capture the imagination of people who like a frightening and spine-chilling horror story.

Although Bram Stoker had used his vivid imagination to dream up Count Dracula, he based the country in which the story is set on a real place.

At the time when Stoker wrote the book Transylvania was a remote part of Hungary.

Set on an isolated plateau and surrounded on all sides by mountains, Transylvania was a secret, almost forgotten place.

The very name 'Transylvania' means 'land beyond the forest'.

In his mind, Stoker conjured up a picture of grim-looking castles surrounded by dark, uninviting forests and woodlands.

He imagined superstitious peasants afraid to leave their homes at night. He saw them sitting round their fires after dark telling each other blood-curdling stories full of horror and terrifying happenings.

It was when Bram Stoker was choosing Transylvania as a setting for his book that he came across the name Dracula. It was an ideal name for him to use for his main character.

Stoker found that just over five hundred years ago part of Transylvania had a ruler called Prince Vlad.

Vlad had been an exceptionally cruel and terrifying figure. He called himself 'Vlad Dracula' since a 'dracul' meant a 'devil' or 'dragon'.

Vlad always carried the sign of the dragon on his shield. He was so feared and hated by his people that they called him 'Vlad the Impaler' because of his unpleasant habit of having anyone who opposed him impaled on a sharpened stake.

During Vlad's reign so many people were killed that it is no wonder that the name 'Dracula' became associated with cruelty and horror.

Using the legend of the vampire bat, borrowing the name Dracula, and setting the story in Transylvania, Stoker had all the ingredients of his horror story.

On an earlier occasion he had met a man whose teeth were like the fangs of a dog. Stoker remembered this, and the sinister Count Dracula came into being!

# King Great Virtue

Long ago, the King of Benares had a son who was
so loving and generous and of such a happy
disposition that everyone who met him could not
help but be glad.

So good and noble was the child's character
that his parents called him Prince Virtue.

Prince Virtue grew into a fine, strong young
man. Not only was he clever, he was also unusually
wise for his age.

When the young prince became king of Benares
he became known as King Great Virtue.

It was easy to see why he was given this name.
Never had there been a king as fair and as just.
Never had the people in the kingdom of Benares
been so happy and contented.

One day, however, King Great Virtue found out
that a minister in his own court had done a
terrible wrong to him and his family.

Another king might have put the minister to death
for his crime. But not King Great Virtue.

Instead, he called for the man and sadly told him
to leave his kingdom for ever. The minister was
allowed to take his wife, his possessions and all
his wealth with him.

'I have been generous and merciful to you,' the
king told him. 'Be the same to others in your new
life. Now go and never return.'

The minister left Benares and went to live in a kingdom called Kosala. Here he worked his way into the King of Kosala's court.

Very soon he found an opportunity to speak to the King of Kosala about King Great Virtue.

'Your Majesty,' he said, hoping to gain favour, 'Since I was so wrongly banished from Benares, I do not mind telling you that the kingdom is like an open door. The king is very weak and even a small army could take his kingdom from him.'

The King of Kosala listened carefully to what the man had told him. Benares was a large and wealthy kingdom. It would certainly be worth his while to conquer it.

Yet suppose this man was a spy being paid to tell him this. If he was not careful he could be led into starting a war that would lose him his country.

He decided to send some men to raid a small town just inside the Benares border. This, he hoped, would tell him if the kingdom was strong and well guarded or not.

The men from Kosala attacked the village but they were soon captured and taken to King Great Virtue himself.

'I am sad you should want to plunder my village,' he told them. 'Why did you do it?'

'Because we are poor and have nothing to live on,' replied the men.

'Then why did you not come to me?' asked King Great Virtue. 'I would not have refused you.'

Instead of punishing them, he gave them gifts. 'Promise never to raid my country again,' he told them, as he set them free.

When the King of Kosala heard this, he rubbed his chin and said, 'This must be a trap. I dare not risk sending an army. I'll send another raiding party. This time they must go deeper into the country.'

Again the raiders were caught and taken to King Great Virtue and just as before he gave them gifts and sent them away.

Now the King of Kosala felt sure he could conquer Benares. 'The king is a fool. He will not resist me by fighting,' he said.

He called his army together and ordered them to prepare to march.

When King Great Virtue heard the news that a great army was moving towards his kingdom, he forbade his warriors to do anything.

'Let the enemy come,' he said. 'We will not resist them, for that would cause bloodshed and hardship. Let those who come seeking kingdoms take them. We shall not fight.'

The King of Kosala marched his army on through the kingdom. 'Let us repel the invasion,' begged King Great Virtue's warriors. 'We are ready to defend you with our lives.'

But the king would not allow any fighting. Even when the army halted outside his city, he still refused to order his men to attack.

To the King of Kosala's amazement the city gates were open. Cautiously he led his army into the city. Inside, all was quiet and peaceful.

He made his way to the palace and, fearing an

ambush, he ordered his best soldiers to lead the way inside.

There they found King Great Virtue seated on his huge throne. Round him, silent and still, were all his ministers.

'We are not armed,' King Great Virtue told the King of Kosala. 'Take the city if you must. We will not fight.'

'Tie up the king and his ministers,' commanded the King of Kosala. 'Dig holes outside the city walls and bury them up to their necks in the ground. In the night, the jackals will come and finish them off.'

Meekly King Great Virtue allowed himself to be tied up and led outside the city. Then all his ministers were bound and led away.

So great was their trust and loyalty to their king that none of them showed any signs of anger or fear.

The enemy soldiers could hardly bear to carry out their orders to bury King Great Virtue and his ministers, who showed nothing but courage and calm dignity.

When the last of the holes was filled in and the earth stamped down, and when the soldiers had left, King Great Virtue called out:

'Do not feel bitter for what has happened today. Have faith!'

That night the jackals came. At once the king and his ministers gave a great shout and the jackals ran off.

But soon the pack came sniffing back when they realised the men were not chasing them, and the pack leader made for the king.

Seeing how unsure the jackal was, the king saw a way to escape. Throwing back his head he exposed his throat as if inviting the creature to bite it.

Before the jackal could bite, however, the king jerked his head forward and bit the jackal first.

Finding himself gripped in the king's strong jaws, the jackal first let out a howl, then struggled to free himself.

Hearing the howl, the jackals backed away and stood uncertain what to do. The king, however, held on tightly and the jackal leader twisted and kicked to free himself.

In doing this, the creature loosened the earth round the king's shoulders. With one arm almost free the king pushed using all his strength. Suddenly the top of his body was out of the earth. Then he let go of the terrified jackal and heaved himself out of the hole.

The jackals fled behind their wounded leader while King Great Virtue freed each minister in turn from the earth.

Now on that particular night, there were demons about. They had come from a place of darkness and they were arguing among themselves.

The ministers were afraid when they heard the demons but king Great Virtue said, 'What have you to fear? The demons will not harm us.'

Indeed, when the demons saw the king, they asked him to settle their argument and this he did.

'Now,' said the king, 'I am dirty. I would like to bathe.'

At once the demons, by their magic powers, fetched scented water which had been set aside for the King of Kosala in the captured palace.

Then the demons brought the robes which had been laid out. They brought the caskets of perfume and the jewels and all kinds of flowers.

And they asked the king what else he would like.

The king told them he was hungry. Using their magic they fetched the supper which had been prepared and they brought with it the scented drinking water with its golden cup and bowl.

And all these things were brought from King Great Virtue's own palace.

After the king had been attended to he said to the demons. 'Deliver each of my ministers to his own home. Then with your magic set me in my own chamber at my palace.'

The demons performed this last task gladly and King Great Virtue found himself in his bedchamber. Asleep in the bed lay the King of Kosala.

King Great Virtue took a sword from the wall. Using the flat of it, he woke the sleeping usurper by striking him several times on the chest.

When the King of Kosala saw who had woken him he was terrified. 'How can this be?' he cried, jumping from the bed. 'I heard from my own men how they left you to the jackals. There are guards outside this chamber. How can you appear before me, fully robed?'

King Great Virtue told how he had escaped his
fate and how he had called on the demons of the
night to help him.

When the King of Kosala heard this he bowed
low before King Great Virtue.

'Forgive me,' he begged. 'I am an unworthy man.
Compared with you I am nothing, even though
I have taken your kingdom. If the night demons
themselves consider you worthy of such respect,
you are indeed great and virtuous.'

With those words he bowed low before King
Great Virtue and asked his forgiveness.

'At first light I shall summon my army and order
them to withdraw. We shall leave your kingdom and
in future you will be safe, for your country will
be honoured among my people.'

After the King of Kosala had left Benares, King
Great Virtue called together all his ministers.

'The victory was ours,' he said proudly. 'We won
it by courage and steadfastness. From now on we
will have peace, and may virtue bring happiness and
prosperity to our land.'

# Canonbie Dick

The moon came out from behind the clouds and a pale silvery light fell on the road. The wind shook a bush by the roadside and rattled the branches of a tree.

'Whoah there! Steady now!' called Canonbie Dick as his two horses plunged and reared.

He took a firmer hold of the horses' halters and led them on along the winding road.

Somewhere in the distance an owl hooted and Canonbie Dick began to sing. From time to time he broke off from his singing to call to the horses or click his tongue as if to help them along the shadowy road.

As he passed a cottage, an upstairs window opened and a man looked out. 'Who's that still about at this time of night?' the man called. He held a lantern above his head. 'Oh it's you, Dick. You're late coming back from market with those two horses.'

Canonbie Dick gave a great shout of laughter and the horses snorted and jerked back their heads.

'I went to sell these horses this morning,' Dick said, 'and I was set to strike a good bargain. I come back with the very same horses this night. No man would give me a fair price.'

'I'd say your price was too high, then,' called the man from the window. 'Your prices are always too high.'

'What do you know about it?' demanded Canonbie Dick. 'These are the finest horses in these parts and I'll not sell them for less than they're worth.'

The man's wife appeared at the window and tugged at her husband's arm. 'Go back to your bed,' she cried. Then she called from the window:

'As for you, Canonbie Dick, you've no right to go disturbing folks from their sleep. No doubt you've spent all your money on drink. You should be home in bed and those poor horses should be safe and warm in their stalls.'

Canonbie Dick blew the woman a kiss and she slammed the window shut in anger.

'Come on, my beauties,' said Dick softly. 'You're fit for a king to ride on and I won't sell you for less than a gentleman would pay.'

Dick passed on through the village whistling merrily. But when he came to a low wall he stopped, for a strange feeling passed over him.

He felt sure someone was watching him.

The horses sensed Dick's uneasiness and both of them stopped. They stiffened their legs and refused to go forwards.

Suddenly a man stood in the road in front of Dick. He seemed to have come from nowhere.

The man was strangely dressed in old-fashioned clothes. His face was hidden from the pale light of the moon by the brim of his hat. He spoke to Dick in a low voice.

'Good morrow, young sir,' he said. 'I need horses fit for a king. Will you sell me yours?'

Dick snatched up a rock from the wall and held it in front of him in fear.

'I'll not strike a bargain at dead of night with a man whose face I cannot see,' he said. 'Be off with you before I give you a sore head.'

The man held out a gold coin in his gloved hand. 'Take it,' he urged. 'You'll find it's gold. I'll give you nine more for the horses.'

Dick felt the weight of the coin. He put it between his teeth and bit on it. It was gold right enough. Dick had never seen a coin like it.

His mind raced. Ten such gold coins must be worth a small fortune.

'Will you take the gold?' asked the man.

'I will,' said Dick. He took the coins and put the horses' halters in the stranger's hand.

A week later Dick set out to sell two more of his horses. Having made such a large sum when he met the stranger on the previous week, he did not care whether he sold the horses at market or not.

He spent some of his gold and returned home late at night leading the horses behind him.

Once again the strange man was waiting for him.

'Good morrow, young sir,' said the stranger. 'I see you have not sold your horses again. Will you sell them to me?'

'I don't know,' said Dick boldly. 'There are no finer horses than these anywhere to be found.'

'Very well,' said the stranger. 'I'll give you twenty pieces of gold for them.'

Dick could hardly believe his luck. He handed the horses to the man and, in exchange, took the gold. Before he had finished counting the coins, the stranger and the horses had disappeared.

The gold turned Canonbie Dick's head and made him greedy. He still had one more horse he could sell and that was his own favourite. It was a fine black stallion.

When market day came around again he said to himself. 'I'll lie in wait for the stranger and if he turns up again I'll sell him this horse. But I'll drive a hard bargain tonight.'

Late that night, Dick waited with his horse by the low stone wall. The minutes dragged by and the black stallion tossed its head and stamped the ground from time to time.

'Perhaps the man won't come tonight,' thought Dick. But then he was startled to find the stranger standing in front of him as if he had appeared from nowhere.

'Do you mean to sell this horse?' asked the man.

'I do if you are willing to pay the right price,' said Dick. 'This is the finest horse I have ever owned.'

The man offered Dick twelve pieces of gold but Dick asked for double that and would take nothing less. For a while they argued, but at last the stranger handed Dick twenty-four gold coins.

Dick could hardly conceal his delight. What was more, he had become curious about the strange man in old-fashioned clothes who appeared at dead of night.

'Why don't we go to your house for a drink to seal the bargain,' suggested Dick.

At that the stranger gave a frightening laugh.

'You can come with me if you've a mind to,' said the man, 'but I must warn you. If your nerve fails then it will be the worse for you.'

With that the man took the horse by the halter and set off up the hill. Dick could see neither the horse nor the man but he followed the sound of the horse's hooves and stumbled after them.

'Wait!' shouted Dick. 'I can't keep up with you.'

At last they came to a great craggy rock that rose up like a sheer wall in front of him.

'Why have you brought me here?' cried Dick gasping for breath.

'Don't let your nerve fail you,' called the man. A hidden door opened in the rock.

The doorway in the rock led into a huge cavern. Canonbie Dick felt himself being drawn inside as if pulled by some giant, invisible hand.

The hidden door closed behind him.

The cavern was like a great hall. Dick could see quite clearly although no lamps or torches burned on the walls.

On either side of the cavern were rows of sleeping horses and knights in armour. The horses stood as still as statues and the knights lay as if frozen at some long-past moment.

Some of the knights had swords in their hands and all carried shields.

One of them was taller than the rest. His hair was white and his armour shone brighter than any other knight.

Canonbie Dick knew that this was King Arthur. He had often heard the legend which tells how Arthur and his knights lie in a magic sleep awaiting the summons to awaken them once again into heroic action.

Dick noticed a table draped with a purple cloth. On it was a sword and a horn. It was then that Dick noticed the stranger and his black horse were nowhere to be seen.

A voice echoed round the cavern. 'You must choose and choose well, Canonbie Dick. Draw the sword or blow the horn. Choose well and thou shalt have luck. Choose ill and misfortune shall overtake thee.'

'Then I will blow the horn,' said Dick, who felt very frightened.

He put the horn to his lips and began to blow it
but the voice cried out, 'Thou hast chosen ill.'

At once a terrible wind picked him up and blew
him out of the cavern. Canonbie Dick was whirled
about like a piece of paper in a gale.

At last he crashed to the ground close to the
very wall where he had first met the stranger.

In the morning some men found him, lying hurt
and bleeding. They carried him home and bathed
his wounds. When they heard his story about the
cavern in the rock with King Arthur and his
knights lying asleep they shook their heads and
left him alone.

# The mystery of Atlantis

One of the greatest mysteries of all time is the story of Atlantis. For almost twenty-four centuries men have wondered whether a great island continent with a highly advanced civilisation once existed in the Atlantic Ocean.

If there was such a place as Atlantis, what happened to it and why has no trace of it ever been found?

It is said that Atlantis disappeared from the face of the earth in a gigantic disaster that lasted just a single day and night.

So great and devasting was this disaster that the island sank beneath the sea, leaving nothing to show that it ever existed.

It is Plato, the Greek philosopher, to whom we owe the story of the lost continent. He heard the strange tale from a statesman called Solon, who in turn heard it from an Egyptian priest.

Plato's account of the island continent as Solon described it to him is so detailed and plausible that, in recent times, men have kept up an almost ceaseless quest to discover its whereabouts.

If there was a flourishing and highly developed continent called Atlantis, what was it like and why did it vanish so suddenly?

Plato describes Atlantis as being an almost perfect place.

Fruits and vegetables grew plentifully in its rich soil. Fragrant flowers and herbs bloomed on the wooded slopes of its beautiful mountains.

All kinds of creatures, both wild and tame, roamed its meadows, plains and hills.

Pure sweet water flowed from underground springs and streams. From some of the springs hot water bubbled up.

The earth was rich in minerals and precious metals and the people of Atlantis used this wealth. Their buildings were skilfully decorated with gold and silver and a strange and beautiful metal called orichalc.

Amid groves and woodlands they set palaces, temples, halls, indoor baths and all manner of public buildings.

They planted gardens and orchards and made pleasant parks and attractive areas for people to walk and play in.

The Atlanteans were skilled engineers. They built a wonderful system of canals all across their country.

One such system linked the capital city, which lay in the centre of the continent, with the sea. A canal was dug from the sea which joined three circular canals built in three rings, one inside the other.

The innermost ring of water surrounded the royal palace and the sacred homes of their ancient gods and goddesses.

The next two rings ran round land on which were built temples, palaces and public buildings.

The canal which came from the sea passed beneath each circle of land under a wide bridge. In this way, ships could sail in to the very heart of the capital.

The Atlanteans loved horses and kept many stables. The horses were used for work and for play and on the largest ring of land a race course ran round the entire circle.

The city in the centre of the continent was surrounded by a vast fertile plain. This, in turn, was ringed entirely by mountains which came down to the sea.

Whether they lived in the city or the country,
the people of Atlantis had everything they could
ever want for their comfort and happiness.

In time, however, their wise and loving ways
were replaced by the need to gain power over the
lands to the east.

They crossed the sea with large armies and
conquered the Mediterranean region and large areas
of North Africa and Europe.

The vast Atlantean army was opposed by a great
force from Athens which beat them back. It was
then that the great cataclysm occurred
which wiped out the entire army in a single day,
and caused Atlantis to sink forever
beneath the waves.

What happened on that fateful day and night which, Plato says, destroyed Atlantis some 11,600 years ago?

Imagine Atlantis as the sun begins to rise at the start of a new day.

In the towns and villages people begin to stir and go about their business.

The great port at the entrance to the sea canal slowly comes to life. Ships and boats move through the water. Men prepare and unload cargo at the many wharves and quaysides.

In the capital city itself the first rays of the sun bathe the glittering rooftops of the temples and palaces in an orange glow.

A slight mist rises from the wooded groves and fragrant gardens.

Then somewhere, deep underground, there comes an ominous rumbling. It shakes the entire continent and people everywhere run out of their houses in alarm.

The sky begins to darken as if a veil had been drawn across it, dimming the rising sun.
The sea has turned the colour of lead. Everywhere a strange choking heat is felt.

There is another rumble. This time it is more violent than the first. People are thrown to the ground, and parts of buildings give way with a shattering series of crashes.

The people panic. Some run into their houses and snatch up a few treasured possessions. Others kneel and pray to their gods.

96

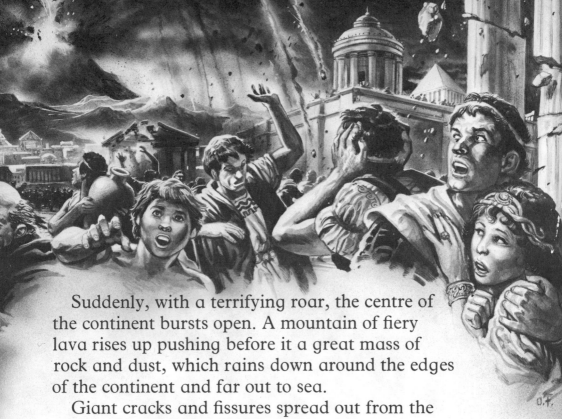

Suddenly, with a terrifying roar, the centre of
the continent bursts open. A mountain of fiery
lava rises up pushing before it a great mass of
rock and dust, which rains down around the edges
of the continent and far out to sea.

Giant cracks and fissures spread out from the
central volcano and the land tilts and heaves.

Buildings collapse and whole towns and villages
slide away as the ground buckles and twists.

The violence of the activity creates enormous
waves in the sea. They sweep over the land, washing
away everything in their path.

Finally the great volcano collapses in on itself
forming a huge crater. Into this crater pours the
sea and slowly the continent of Atlantis begins
to sink beneath the angry waves.

In twenty four hours the violence is spent and
nothing remains but a cloud of black ash in the
sky and a churning sea.

Beneath the seething water, lost forever, is the
once proud continent of Atlantis.

# How Banjuwangi got its name

On the East coast of Java, close to the Island of
Bali lies the city of Banjuwangi. It is there that
a river flows down from the mountains, through the
forest and on into the sea.

The name Banjuwangi has a special meaning, for
'Banju' means 'water', and 'wangi' means 'scented'.
Together the two words give that place the name
'scented water'.

There is a story which tells how Banjuwangi was
given its name.

Many years ago, a king ruled this part of Java. One of his governors was a keen and hard working young man called Sidapaksa.

There were two things in Sidapaksa's life which he loved more than anything else. One was his work as governor in which he served the king faithfully and well. The other was his young and beautiful wife whom he adored as much as she adored him.

When one day Sidapaksa's wife told him she was to have a baby, the young governor was overjoyed. There could not have been a happier man in all Java.

'Soon I shall have three loves,' he said to himself. 'My work, my wife and now a little child.'

There was, however, one black cloud which hung over the young couple's happy life together. This was the hatred which Sidapaksa's mother felt for her son's lovely young wife.

The mother was a vain and proud old woman. She was full of ambition for her son.

The young wife came from a poor and humble home. The old woman felt she was not good enough for her son. 'He should have married someone of rank and position,' she said bitterly.

She began to brood and scheme, hoping to think of a way to break up her son's marriage.

When she heard that the couple were to have a child, her hatred grew even more.

'Now I must turn Sidapaksa against his wife at all costs,' she thought. 'Perhaps I will be able to use the child to turn him against her.'

At last an idea formed in her wicked mind. But first, as part of her evil plan, she had to make sure Sidapaksa would not be there when the child was born.

She went to see the king and persuaded him to send her son away on an important mission.

That night, Sidapaksa spoke to his wife with a heavy heart. 'The king has ordered me to seek a flower which, he has heard, grows on the top of Mount Idjen.

'The flower has magic properties. It has the power to make its owner for ever young and good-looking. The king wants the flower for his wife.'

'But our baby is soon to be born,' cried Sidapaksa's wife, sobbing in his arms. 'Will you not be here when I need you most?'

'Alas,' said Sidapaksa. 'I cannot disobey the king. I must leave at once. The mission is difficult and dangerous. I will be gone for several months.'

Sidapaksa's mother had been hiding behind a screen as her son broke the sad news to his wife.

A cruel smile twisted across her face and she rubbed her bony hands together with satisfaction.

The next day, Sidapaksa bade a sorrowful farewell to his wife. Before he left he asked his mother to look after her for him.

The old woman put her arm round the girl and held her close to her skinny body. 'Is she not soon to have my grandchild?' she asked. 'I shall look after her with all the love I show to you, my son.'

Sidapaksa rode away not suspecting the evil that lay in the old woman's heart.

A few days later, the baby was born. It was a fine bonny son. 'If only my husband were here,' sighed the wife. 'How proud he would be to see such a beautiful son.'

Now the baby was safely born, all the wicked old woman had to do was wait for the right moment. Then she could put her plan to work.

The time came some weeks later. The young mother, after seeing that her baby was fast asleep, went to bathe in the river.

As soon as she was gone, the old woman crept into the house and took hold of the sleeping baby. Then she hurried to the river with him. She made sure nobody was watching.

Without hesitating, she threw the baby into the deepest part of the water. At once he sank from sight under the muddy water.

The poor unsuspecting girl returned from her bathe and, straight away, went to see if her son was still asleep.

The sight of the empty cot filled her with panic and horror. Where was her baby?

She dashed from room to room looking desperately for her child. She sent servants rushing this way and that in a frantic search. None of them could think how or why the baby had gone. None of them could find it.

'Can the baby have been stolen?' people asked.

The young mother could no longer rest or sleep. She blamed herself for leaving the baby alone. She went on searching and searching although she knew it was quite hopeless.

At last she fell ill from grief and exhaustion and had to be carried to her bed.

The wicked old woman now began to poison the minds of her daughter-in-law's servants and friends.

'Who would steal a baby?' she whispered. 'What proof is there it was stolen? Maybe she lost the baby in the river. After all, that is where she went that day.'

Soon, people began to turn against the young girl and her grief and illness grew worse.

At last news came that Sidapaksa was shortly to
return home. His mother kept the news to herself
and waited in the courtyard for him when he arrived.

There she told her son cruel lies about his wife.
'You were a fool to marry a common girl from such
humble parents,' she said.

'She was incapable of looking after your baby
son. Instead she took the poor little thing and let
it drown in the river.

'Of course she tried to make out that someone
stole him away, but I know better.

'Now she has taken to her bed. She pretends to
be ill, hoping that we will all feel sorry for her.'

The old woman wove such a web of lies about her daughter-in-law that Sidapaksa began to believe her.

He had no reason to suppose that his mother would lie to her own son, nor did he realise how wicked and cruel she was.

'Go to your wife and surprise her,' urged the old woman. 'Perhaps the shock of seeing you will make her confess her wickedness.'

Stirred to anger by his mother's words, Sidapaksa drew a knife from his belt and burst into his young wife's room.

'What have you done with my child?' he shouted.
'You let him drown in the river, confess it!' And
seizing his wife, he held the knife to her heart.

Numb with shock at Sidapaksa's sudden and furious
return, the young wife could not speak.

'See,' crowed the old woman who had followed
her son into the room. 'She admits her guilt by
saying nothing.'

At this the girl found her voice. 'My husband!'
she cried. 'Why should you think such a thing of
me? Why should I harm our son, whom I loved more
than I love my own life?'

'Don't listen to her,' hissed the old woman. 'Kill
her at once for she has brought enough shame on you
as it is.'

'Oh husband!' sobbed the girl. 'Before you went
away, did we not love each other? Why should you
want to kill me now? If you believe I had anything
to do with our son's death, take me to the river
now. I will show you I am innocent.'

'Beware, Sidapaksa,' cried the old woman.
'She will trick you as she has tricked us all
in the past.'

But Sidapaksa wanted to give his wife the chance
to prove her innocence. Lifting her in his arms, he
carried her down to the water's edge. There he put
her down and said, 'Now what is it you wish to
show me?'

Without a word, his wife threw herself into the
deep water and sank from sight.

Sidapaksa beat his breast and wept bitter tears.
'Alas!' he cried. 'I have lost both my son and my
wife. Now I will never know the truth.'

Torn with grief, he stood gazing and gazing at the deep muddy river.

'Come home, my son,' said the old woman plucking at his sleeve. What has happened is for the best, you will see.'

Suddenly, from the depths of the river there rose two beautiful white flowers on delicate green stems.

They gave out a wonderful perfume and their fragrance filled the air.

The taller of the two flowers spoke.

'See, Sidapaksa,' it said. 'The flower beside me is our son. He will tell you how he met so cruel a death.'

Then the smaller of the flowers spoke.

'Oh father,' it said. 'I died because of the pride and vanity of your own mother. It was she who stole me away and cast me into the river. She hated my mother and plotted to end your marriage.'

Sidapaksa gave a great sob, but the small flower said. 'My mother and I are happy now for we will never be parted.'

And with that the two lovely flowers sank back under the water.

These two flowers were never seen again, nor
have any like them ever been seen since. However,
the perfume which they gave out remained behind.

Later, people who came to bathe in the river
were astonished at the fragrance of the water.

# How the lord chose a wife

There once lived in Scotland a lord who fell on hard times. He had to sell a good many of his estates. His workers became lazy and indifferent to him. The castle fell into disrepair and his land became neglected and overgrown.

When the lord died his son, who had been in another country for several years, returned to Scotland to take his father's title and become the new lord.

The young man was dismayed when he saw the state of the castle and its lands. But being a strong-minded and determined sort of person, he decided to restore the castle and return the land to its former good use.

He worked hard for many months and gradually, by his efforts, made great improvements.

One day he said to himself, 'What I need now is a good wife. But what kind of wife should I choose? She will need to be a very special kind of girl.'

At last the young lord had an idea. He found a suit of old ragged clothes and put it on. He smudged his face with dirt and put a greasy cap on his head.

Looking no better than a tramp, he set off in search of a wife.

When he came to a house or cottage he would knock on the door. If a girl answered it, he would say, 'Have pity on me. I am a poor man. I have not touched food for two days. Look! I am in rags.'

The first girl he spoke to in this way went and fetched him bread and cheese and a cup of milk.

The young lord thanked her and went on his way but he said to himself, 'That is not the girl for me.'

The next girl to answer her door to him went and fetched him a coat. 'I have no food to give you,' she said, 'but at least this coat will keep you warm.'

The lord thanked her and took the coat but he went on his way thinking, 'That is not the girl for me either.'

At several more houses he begged from the girls who came to the door. All took pity on him and the young lord began to wonder if he would ever find the girl he was seeking.

Then he came to a small cottage. A kind-looking girl opened the door. In a choking voice with his eyes brimming with tears, the young lord said:

'Take pity on me. I am a poor beggar. I have had nothing to eat for two days. Look, I am in rags. Give me some food or some clothing.'

The girl looked closely at him. She saw that his shoulders were broad and his arms were strong.

'Yes,' she said, 'I have something for you.' She picked up a broom and started to beat the young lord as hard as she could.

'This is what I give to a lazy good-for-nothing like you,' she cried. 'Go and work for your living and you will suffer neither hunger nor cold.'

Then she slammed the door in his face.

The young lord was delighted. 'This is the girl for me,' he said. He went home, washed his face and put on his best clothes.

Then he went once again to the girl's cottage and asked her to become his wife. And after they were married he knew that his choice was the right one.

# Eros the secret husband

One of the ancient Greek stories tells how there was once a king who had three daughters. The oldest two were good looking but Psyche, the youngest, was so lovely that her beauty was quite dazzling.

She was so beautiful that people compared her looks with those of Aphrodite, the goddess of beauty.

When Aphrodite heard this she grew angry and jealous. 'Is my beauty to be overshadowed by a mortal girl?' she cried indignantly.

She summoned her son Eros, the god of love, and told him to fly down to earth and punish the proud Psyche.

Eros took two small jars and went to the fountains in Aphrodite's garden. One he filled with the bitter waters of shame. The other he filled with the sweet waters of joy.

Then he flew off to do his mother's bidding.

It was dark by the time he reached the king's palace. Stealthily he crept into Psyche's room and shed a few drops of bitter water on the sleeping girl's lips.

At that moment the moon shone through the open window and lit up the princess. At once Eros fell deeply in love with her. Sorry for what he had done, he poured some of the sweet water of joy over Psyche's hair.

Just then Psyche awoke and, although Eros was invisible to her, it seemed to him as if she stared straight at him.

In confusion he wounded himself with the tip of his deadly arrow as he hastened away.

From then on Psyche was still the subject of much admiration but now she felt no love for any man and no man fell in love with her.

Time passed and while both her sisters married happily, Psyche remained unloved.

Her parents grew anxious and feared that they had angered the gods in some way. They consulted an oracle who told them that Psyche's husband was not to be a man but a monster who waited for her at the top of a mountain.

Sadly Psyche decided to go to the mountain to meet her fate but as she stood on the edge of a cliff a gentle wind lifted her up and carried her to a beautiful valley full of flowers.

In the valley she discovered a beautiful palace where servants bade her enter and eat the banquet they had prepared for her.

That night, Eros flew down to the valley and in the
darkness told Psyche tenderly that he loved her.
He said that he would be a loving husband to her
but would only visit her after dark and would leave
before dawn broke.

He begged her never to try to find out who he was.
If she did so, he would leave her and never return.

One night Psyche told Eros that although she
was happy she longed to see her two sisters again.
Eros promised to grant her wish.

Eros commanded the South Wind to bring Psyche's
sisters to the valley and the next morning they
appeared before Psyche who greeted them warmly.

When the three had recovered from their surprise
they sat down and talked. Psyche told her sisters
about her secret husband.

At once the sisters asked Psyche what this man
looked like and who he was.

Psyche felt abashed at having to tell them that
she did not know the answer to either question.
Her sisters reminded her of the words of the
oracle.

'Why, this man could well be a terrible monster.'
said one. 'You must take a lamp and shine it on
him while he is asleep. That way you will find out
if he is a monster or not.'

Much against her will, Psyche was persuaded to
hide a lamp in her room so that she could look at
her husband as he slept. She also concealed a
dagger with which to kill him should he be
a hideous monster.

That night, Psyche waited for Eros to fall
asleep then she took the lamp and shone it on him.
She saw before her the handsome young god of love
with his winged shoulders.

She was overcome with shame for breaking her word.

At that moment a drop of hot oil spilt from the lamp on to Eros's shoulder and woke him. When he saw Psyche standing over him with a lamp he was angry and disappointed.

He spread his wings and flew through the window. Psyche ran after him but he called, 'I will punish you by leaving you for ever.'

Psyche was overwhelmed with sorrow at her folly and waited, heartbroken, for Eros to return. Night after night she waited but he did not come to her.

Psyche wandered away from the valley in search of her husband and at last met Ceres, the goddess of the earth.

Ceres told her that Eros went to Aphrodite, his mother, every day to have the burn on his shoulder cleaned and dressed.

'Go to Aphrodite,' Ceres urged Psyche. 'She is angry with you, but plead with her and beg for mercy.'

Psyche took the goddess's advice, but Aphrodite was still jealous and angry with the beautiful young girl.

The goddess gave Psyche a number of impossible tasks to carry out. Each time, Eros secretly helped her to accomplish the tasks but this angered Aphrodite.

She ordered Psyche to go to the underworld and bring back a certain box of beauty ointment.

Psyche did so but she thought the ointment would smooth away the marks of all the tears she had shed over Eros. Despite being warned not to open the box she carefully pulled up the lid to take some of the ointment.

The box did not contain beauty ointment, however, but the spirit of sleep. Immediately, Psyche fell asleep by the roadside.

Eros, watching over Psyche, found her and replaced the spirit of sleep in the box. Then he woke Psyche and took her to Aphrodite while he himself flew to the king of the gods and pleaded with him to allow Psyche to become his immortal bride.

The king was moved by the plea of Eros and he
persuaded Aphrodite to accept Psyche as her
daughter-in-law.

Aphrodite forgot her early jealousy and gave her
consent and blessing. The gods made Psyche immortal
and she and Eros were never again parted.

# The legend of fair Rosamund

Queen Eleanor's eyes flashed angrily. 'Who is this
girl who comes between me and my husband?'

The knight stared at the ground and shifted his
weight from one foot to the other.

The queen's voice cracked out like a whip. 'Speak
out, sir knight, before I have you flogged.'

'My lady, the king has built a bower just outside
the walls of his palace at Woodstock. It is there
that Rosamund lives. The king visits her whenever
he can.'

The queen bit her lip and her fingers tightened on the perfumed lace handkerchief she was holding. 'Go on, sir knight,' she said. 'Tell me more.'

The knight looked up and his eyes met those of the queen. Her cold angry stare sent a stab of fear through him.

'The maid Rosamund is of matchless beauty,' he said. 'People call her Rosa Mundi, the rose of the world. She is indeed the fairest damsel I have ever seen.' Once again he stared at the ground.

The queen rose to her feet. 'Very well,' she said. 'Take me at once to Woodstock and show me the bower where my husband, the king, keeps the fair Rosamund.'

'My lady!' stammered the knight. 'I will take you but you will not be able to see Rosamund.'

Again the queen's eyes flashed in anger. 'Who would dare to stop me?' she cried. 'King Henry, my husband, is away at war. Nobody in the land will prevent me from entering the bower.'

'It is not that, my lady,' replied the knight. 'The king has set the bower in the middle of a maze of underground passages. They say the maze has as many as a hundred and fifty dead ends. No one dare enter it for fear of being lost. Only Sir Thomas, your husband's most trusted knight, knows his way through the labyrinth to Rosamund's bower.'

'Nevertheless, I order you to take me to Woodstock at once,' demanded the queen. 'I shall find a way to reach the maid Rosamund, come what may.'

Some days later Queen Eleanor hid herself near the entrance to the labyrinth. As she watched secretly she saw Sir Thomas emerge.

In his hand was a ball of silken thread which he unwound as he went. The Queen knew at once that the thread led the way through the maze of tunnels to where Rosamund was hidden.

Queen Eleanor ordered her men to seize Sir Thomas. Then, taking with her a sword and a cup of poison, she followed the silk thread until she came to the heart of the labyrinth.

There she found Rosamund busily engaged in embroidery.

'Now, vixen!' cried the Queen. 'Prepare to die.

You may choose either the sword or the poison cup.
Which shall it be?'

Rosamund pleaded with the queen to punish her
in some way and begged that her life be spared.

Queen Eleanor was moved by the loveliness
of Rosamund's face, but her jealousy overcame her
pity. 'Choose the poison or the sword,' she said.

Without another word, Rosamund took the cup
of poison and drank it down.

When she was dead, Queen Eleanor wept with
remorse at the death of such a beautiful girl, and
sorrow took the place of her jealous anger.

'She was indeed the fairest of maids,' the
Queen confessed.

# The emergency

There was one important rule in the school. It was
that the boys and girls were never to run when
they were inside the building.

'Always walk,' the headmaster would insist.
'Never, NEVER let me catch any of you running in
the corridor unless there is an emergency.'

One day, just as the headmaster was coming out
of his room, a boy rushed along the corridor as
fast as he could.

The headmaster grabbed the boy and held him by
the ear. 'I thought I told you never to run unless
there is an emergency,' he boomed.

'That's right, sir,' panted the boy. 'There is
an emergency. 'I've got to stop two boys from
fighting.'

'Very well,' said the headmaster, and he relaxed
his hold on the boy's ear. 'Who are these two boys?'

'One of them is me, sir,' called the boy as he
dashed off.